Culinary Essentials

Culinary Vocabulary Skills

McGraw Hill Glencoe

New York, New York   Columbus, Ohio   Chicago, Illinois   Peoria, Illinois   Woodland Hills, California

Note to Culinary Instructors

A *Word Challenge* puzzle has been created for each Section and Unit of the ***Culinary Essentials*** text. The puzzle clues will enable students to practice their culinary vocabulary skills. *Word Challenge Answers* are included at the back of this ancillary.

 **Glencoe**

The *McGraw-Hill* Companies

Send all inquiries to:
Glencoe/McGraw-Hill
3008 W. Willow Knolls Drive
Peoria, IL 61614-1083

ISBN 0-07-869077-3

Printed in the United States of America

1 2 3 4 5 6 7 8 9 024 08 07 06 05 04

Contents

Contents, continued

Word Challenge 1-1

Directions: Complete the crossword puzzle using the vocabulary clues provided below.

Across

3 Provide a variety of work experiences
   (2 words)
5 Chef in charge of cold foods

Down

1 Chef's assistant
2 Seller to the foodservice industry
4 Team of foodservice specialists

Word Challenge 1-2

Directions: Complete the crossword puzzle using the vocabulary clues provided below.

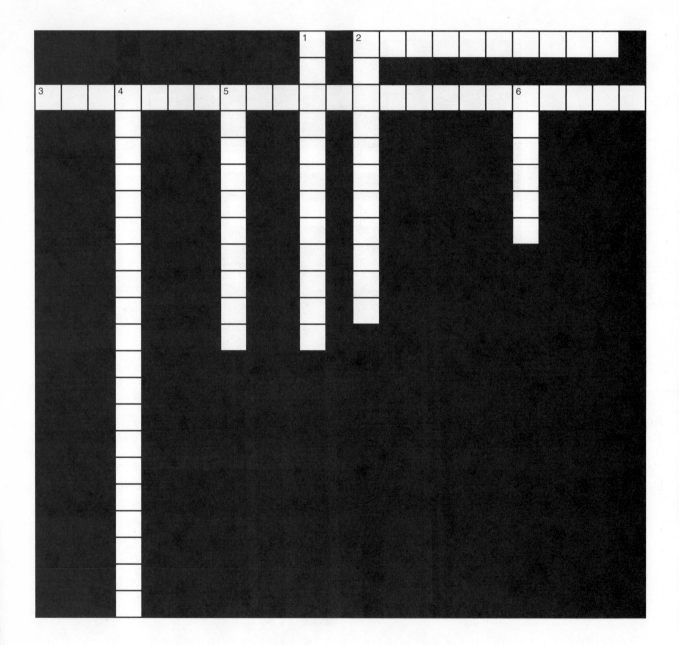

Across

2 Excellent food in a fashionable setting
   (2 words)
3 Operations designed only to cover costs
   (2 words)

Down

1 Fast, economical food provided *(2 words)*
2 Restaurant that employs servers
4 Businesses that intend to make money
   (2 words)
5 Typical "first" jobs *(2 words)*
6 Tendencies within an industry

Culinary Vocabulary Skills

Word Challenge 1-3

Directions: Rearrange each set of letters to form a word. When all the correct words are in place, you will see the vocabulary word in the shaded column.

1. TACINARLIPO
2. TELRET
3. TOREMN
4. VELATEAU
5. LIFAQYU
6. SORFM
7. RIWTINVEE
8. ACERETH
9. INGANITR
10. UGLEARSONIT
11. PATRICCE
12. PAMDOLI
13. CANDENTATE

HINT: Official recognition

1. RANEL
2. PAPYL
3. ROOFISEPSN
4. ARRPMOG
5. YEMPELEO
6. SSNGITMANE
7. NADRADST
8. HIYENEG
9. ARNEPAAPEC
10. MUSEER

HINT: Trainee

Word Challenge 1-4

Directions: Complete the crossword puzzle using the vocabulary clues provided below.

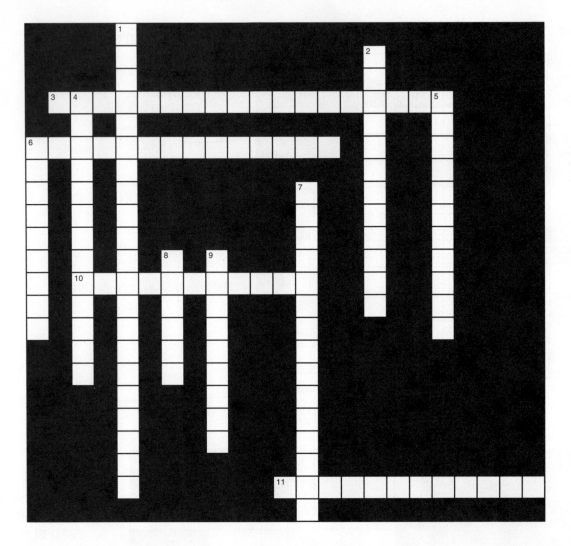

Across

3. One-owner system *(2 words)*
6. System with little government control *(2 words)*
10. Government-chartered business
11. "Self-starter" who runs a business

Down

1. Non-chain restaurant *(2 words)*
2. How a business is geared to perform *(2 words)*
4. Expenses beyond food and labor *(2 words)*
5. Business with two or more owners
6. License to sell a company's products
7. Restaurant with the same name and "look" as others *(2 words)*
8. System of limiting land use
9. How customers know about products and services

Culinary Vocabulary Skills

Word Challenge 2-1

Directions: Complete the crossword puzzle using the vocabulary clues provided below.

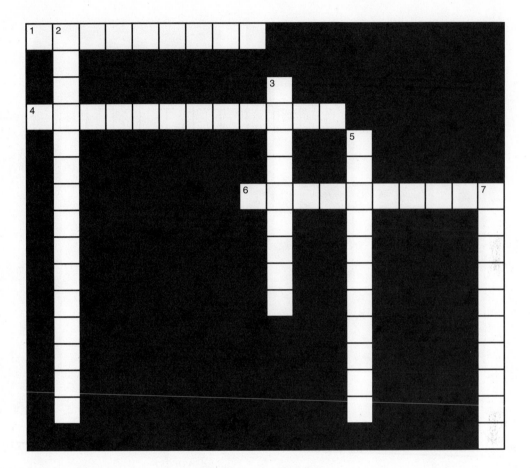

Across

1 To work with numbers
4 Things that hinder listening
6 Motivating others toward a common goal

Down

2 Paying close attention to a speaker (*2 words*)
3 Intention to do your best at work (*2 words*)
5 Adapting to changing circumstances
7 Put things in order of importance

Word Challenge 2-2

Directions: Complete the crossword puzzle using the vocabulary clues provided below.

Across

4 Magazines produced by and for an industry *(2 words)*

Down

1 Meeting of an applicant and employer *(2 words)*
2 Employment opportunity *(2 words)*
3 Terms used in an electronic search *(2 words)*
5 Summary of an applicant's qualifications
6 Making contacts to reach career goals

Word Challenge 2-3

Directions: Complete the crossword puzzle using the vocabulary clues provided below.

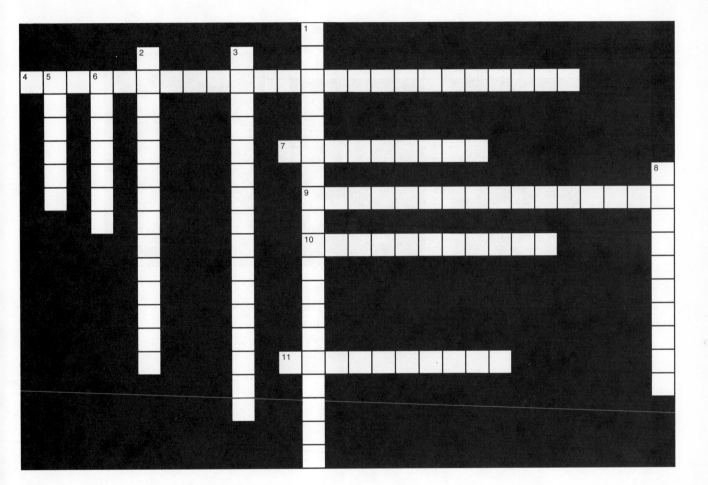

Across

4 Ailments due to repeating the same motion *(3 words)*
7 Period for evaluation of a new worker
9 Payback for overtime work *(2 words)*
10 Lowest rate of pay *(2 words)*
11 Organized group of workers *(2 words)*

Down

1 Financial support for injured employees *(2 words)*
2 Unfair treatment based on some prejudice
3 Unwelcome sexual behavior *(2 words)*
5 Personal basis for knowing right from wrong
6 Skill of putting yourself in another's shoes
8 Monies withheld from your paycheck

Word Challenge 3-1

Directions: Complete the crossword puzzle using the vocabulary clues provided below.

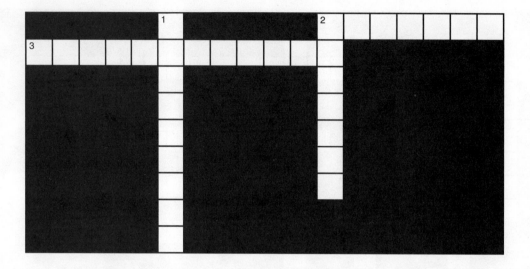

Across
2 Another word for section
3 Communicating by physical action
   (2 words)

Down
1 Customer support
2 Server's group of tables

Name _____ Date _____

Word Challenge 3-2

Directions: Complete the crossword puzzle using the vocabulary clues provided below.

Across
4 To set a table before serving food
6 Emphasizing a menu item

Down
1 One place setting
2 Meal's first course
3 Suggesting the customer buy more or better food
5 Dish placed beneath another

Word Challenge 3-3

Directions: Complete the crossword puzzle using the vocabulary clues provided below.

Across

3 Strong coffee beverage
4 Using hot liquid to extract flavors

Down

1 Espressso-and-milk beverage
2 Espresso cup

Word Challenge 4-1

Directions: Complete the crossword puzzle using the vocabulary clues provided below.

Across

1 Mall area of quick-service restaurants
   (2 words)
2 Seating with chair backs against a wall
4 To "flame" a food tableside
6 Very small appetizers

Down

1 Server's "center" *(2 words)*
3 Next to the dining table
5 Food pan sitting above a canned
   heat source *(2 words)*

Word Challenge 4-2

Directions: Complete the crossword puzzle using the vocabulary clues provided below.

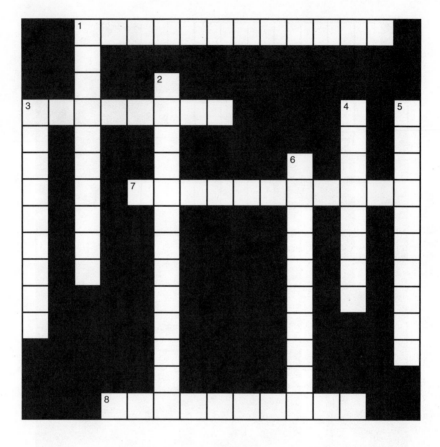

Across

1 Table decorations
3 Duties performed before opening a
   dining room *(2 words)*
7 Rapidly heated and cooled glass *(2 words)*
8 Meal selections made before arrival
   (2 words)

Down

1 Food accompaniments
2 Foods that won't spoil quickly
3 Napkin-covered plate used to carry
   flatware
4 Dining utensils
5 Branched candlestick
6 Describes foods that can spoil quickly

Word Challenge 5-1

Directions: Complete the crossword puzzle using the vocabulary clues provided below.

Across

5 Scheduling too many workers *(2 words)*
7 Total costs equal total income *(2 words)*

Down

1 Staff *(2 words)*
2 Prediction of expenses, need, or profit
3 Business financial report *(4 words)*
4 Employee wages *(2 words)*
6 Labor costs beyond wages *(2 words)*

Word Challenge 5-2

Directions: Complete the crossword puzzle using the vocabulary clues provided below.

Across

2 Familiarizing employees with facility and job

3 Tutors of new employees

Down

1 Praise for a job well done *(2 words)*

Culinary Vocabulary Skills

Word Challenge 5-3

Directions: Complete the crossword puzzle using the vocabulary clues provided below.

Across

2   Moving past unrelated stations when serving

Down

1   How often a seat is occupied (*2 words*)
2   Space to meet customer and staff needs

Word Challenge 5-4

Directions: Complete the crossword puzzle using the vocabulary clues provided below.

Across

2   Restaurants owned by the same company that sell the same products
3   Main customers
4   Advertising by mail *(2 words)*
5   A geographic area
10 Publicity and advertising *(2 words)*

Down

1   License to sell a company's products
6   The "feel" that customers get from a facility
7   Presentation of a business to its community
8   Businesses with similar products
9   Free or low-cost promotion
11 Paid form of promotion

Culinary Vocabulary Skills

Word Challenge 6-1

Directions: Complete the crossword puzzle using the vocabulary clues provided below.

Across

2 Rating food products
3 Recognized norms
6 Food deliberately exposed to radiation *(2 words)*

Down

1 Records of hazardous chemicals *(4 words)*
2 Foods made by recombining genes *(2 words)*
4 Government rules for food quality
5 Discarded materials *(2 words)*

Word Challenge 6-2

Directions: Complete the crossword puzzle using the vocabulary clues provided below.

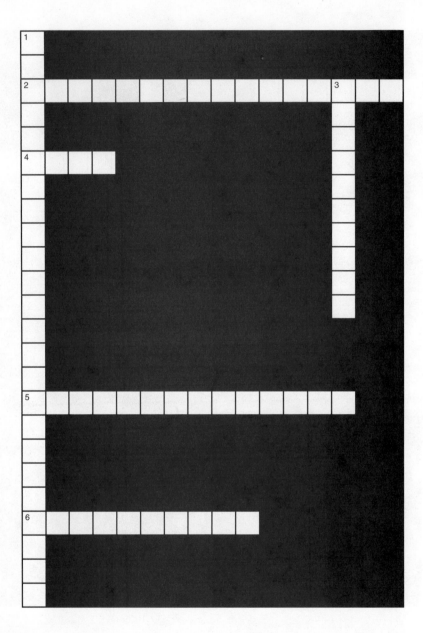

Across

2   Unwelcome sexual behavior in the workplace *(2 words)*
4   Legal rules against discrimination
5   Unfair treatment due to prejudice
6   Bodily condition that limits activity

Down

1   Conditions caused by repetitious movement *(2 words)*
3   The study of how people and things interact

Culinary Vocabulary Skills

Name_____ Date _____

Word Challenge 7-1

Directions: Complete the crossword puzzle using the vocabulary clues provided below.

Across

2 Preventing use of faulty electrical equipment *(2 words)*
5 Tearing away of a body part
7 Deep skin cut
8 Emergency care to restore air and blood flow *(2 words)*

Down

1 Quick-to-burn materials
3 A scrape or minor cut
4 Deep hole in the skin
6 Action to aid a choking victim *(2 words)*

Word Challenge 7-2

Directions: Complete the crossword puzzle using the vocabulary clues provided below.

Across

3 Spoilage from direct exposure *(2 words)*
8 Keeping work space clean
10 Single-celled organisms that might cause illness
11 Procedure to limit surface contaminants

Down

1 Tiny organisms found everywhere
2 Clean
4 Unsafe
5 Spoilage caused by microorganism transfer *(2 words)*
6 Harmful substances
7 Source of danger
9 Small organisms that live off other organisms

Culinary Vocabulary Skills

Word Challenge 8-1

Directions: Rearrange each set of letters to form a word. When all the correct words are in place, you will see the vocabulary word in the shaded column.

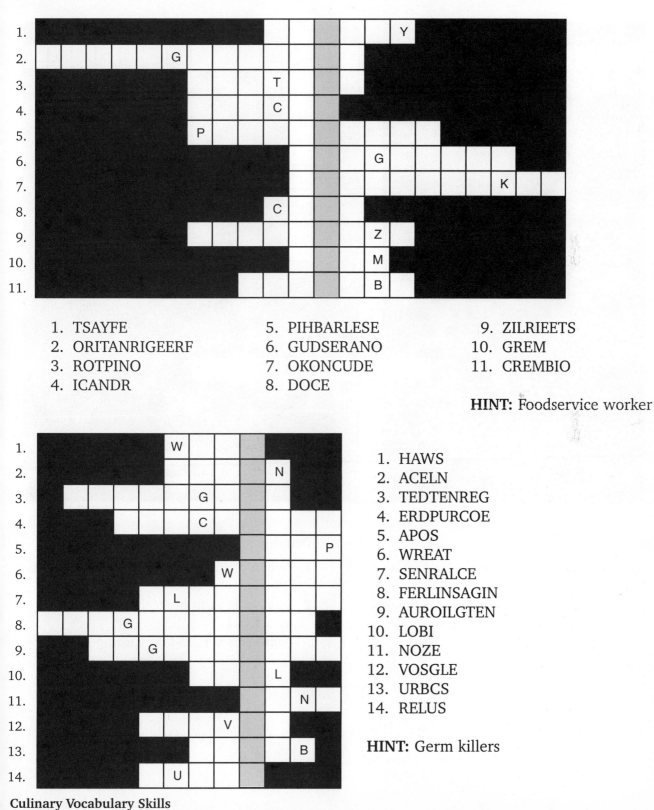

1. TSAYFE
2. ORITANRIGEERF
3. ROTPINO
4. ICANDR

5. PIHBARLESE
6. GUDSERANO
7. OKONCUDE
8. DOCE

9. ZILRIEETS
10. GREM
11. CREMBIO

HINT: Foodservice worker

1. HAWS
2. ACELN
3. TEDTENREG
4. ERDPURCOE
5. APOS
6. WREAT
7. SENRALCE
8. FERLINSAGIN
9. AUROILGTEN
10. LOBI
11. NOZE
12. VOSGLE
13. URBCS
14. RELUS

HINT: Germ killers

Culinary Vocabulary Skills

Word Challenge 8-2

Directions: Complete the crossword puzzle using the vocabulary clues provided below.

Across

4 Lowest temperature to attain food safety
   (3 words)
5 Food thermometer that has been adjusted
   correctly

Down

1 When contamination might occur
   (3 words)
2 Path of food from receiving to disposal
   (3 words)
3 Foodservice food-safety rating system

Culinary Vocabulary Skills

Word Challenge 8-3

Directions: Complete the crossword puzzle using the vocabulary clues provided below.

Across

2 Spoils quickly
6 Holding food for later use

Down

1 Accepting deliveries
3 Keeping cooked food warm until needed
4 Heated to destroy harmful bacteria
5 How stock is rotated

Word Challenge 9-1

Directions: Complete the crossword puzzle using the vocabulary clues provided below.

Across

4 Area with all the tools and equipment for a set of tasks *(2 words)*

6 Most efficient way to perform tasks *(2 words)*

7 Orderly movement in the kitchen *(2 words)*

Down

1 French for "to put in place" *(3 words)*

2 Kitchen equipment arrangement *(2 words)*

3 Groups of work stations *(2 words)*

5 Least movement with minimal effort *(3 words)*

Word Challenge 9-2

Directions: Rearrange each set of letters to form a word. When all the correct words are in place, you will see the vocabulary word in the shaded column.

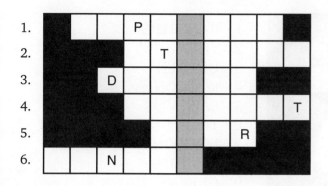

1. PLUSSIPE
2. ORATGES
3. WADRER
4. BETCAIN
5. ODOR
6. TYPRAN

HINT: Short refrigerator

1. EGIRFEERRAT
2. PARMETRUTEE
3. TEWAS
4. PRYDATEHE
5. ROZE
6. TAME
7. OROCL
8. BATVELGEES
9. ILQTAUY
10. PAWPINGR
11. GNARED

HINT: Cold damage

Culinary Vocabulary Skills

Word Challenge 9-3

Directions: Rearrange each set of letters to form a word. When all the correct words are in place, you will see the vocabulary word in the shaded column.

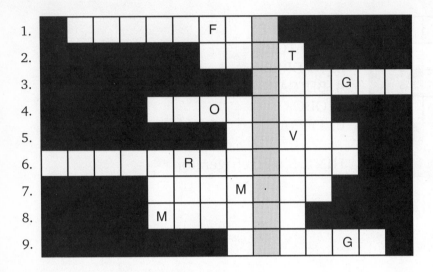

1. RANFETRS
2. THEA
3. GRADEN
4. KOGCONI
5. SAWEV
6. TRERPSAVNEOI
7. MAGWINR
8. TEMDHO
9. GREENY

HINT: Transfer energy

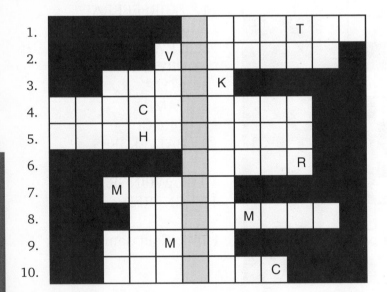

1. MESUTIN
2. BRAVEIT
3. CKIQU
4. TONCIRLEEC
5. ETONGOLCHY
6. EWRAT
7. AMELT
8. MEVMOTEN
9. MITER
10. SACTIPL

HINT: Invisible waves of energy

Culinary Vocabulary Skills

Name_____   Date _____

Word Challenge 9-4

Directions: Complete the crossword puzzle using the vocabulary clues provided below.

Across

2 Food container that controls temperature and humidity *(3 words)*

Down

1 Serving line food warmer *(2 words)*
3 Water bath that keeps liquids warm *(2 words)*

Word Challenge 10-1

Directions: Complete the crossword puzzle using the vocabulary clues provided below.

Across

3 Knife sharpening stone
4 Small cubes made from julienne slices
5 Area where knife blade and handle merge
8 Knife blade within the handle
10 Matchstick-shaped cuts, ⅛-inch thick

Down

1 To finely slice vegetables
2 Keeping a blade straight after sharpening
4 Matchstick-shaped cuts, ¼-inch thick
6 Knife handle fasteners
7 Disk-shaped slice
9 Saw-toothed blade

Name_____   Date _____

Word Challenge 10-2

Directions: Complete the crossword puzzle using the vocabulary clues provided below.

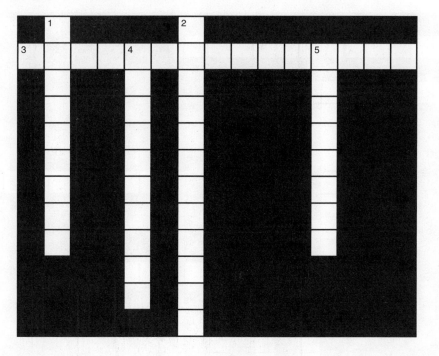

Across

3   Melon baller with a scoop at each end
    (2 words)

Down

1   Handheld cooking and serving items
    (2 words)
2   Heat passage between objects *(2 words)*
4   Hand tools, pots, and pans
5   Pots and pans

Word Challenge 11-1

Directions: Complete the crossword puzzle using the vocabulary clues provided below.

Across

2 Fats that are liquid at room temperature
3 Adding hydrogen to change oil into solid fat
5 Main source of food energy
8 Fats that are solid at room temperature (*2 words*)
10 Pods containing seeds

Down

1 Type of fat in sunflower and soybean oil
4 Substances added to improve foods
5 Fatty substances found in animal foods
6 Substances in food that help the body function
7 Heart-related
9 Protein building blocks

Culinary Vocabulary Skills

Word Challenge 11-2

Directions: Complete the crossword puzzle using the vocabulary clues provided below.

Across

2 Vegetarians who eat dairy products and eggs *(2 words)*
9 Fluid imbalance

Down

1 Nutrients needed per day *(2 words)*
2 Vegetarians who eat some dairy products, but not eggs *(2 words)*
3 Vegetarians who eat eggs *(2 words)*
4 People who don't eat meat
5 Strict vegetarians
6 Storage form of glucose
7 Low-calorie, high-nutrient food *(2 words)*
8 Chemicals in food that may fight disease

Culinary Vocabulary Skills

Word Challenge 11-3

Directions: Complete the crossword puzzle using the vocabulary clues provided below.

Across

2   Foods processed into a smooth pulp
3   Preparing food in small amounts as needed
    (2 words)

Down

1   Dissolve

Name_____ Date _____

Word Challenge 12-1

Directions: Complete the crossword puzzle using the vocabulary clues provided below.

Across

3 Menu with separate appetizer and dessert prices *(5 words)*
9 Menus with full-meal prices and some options *(3 words)*
10 List of food choices

Down

1 Long-term menu *(2 words)*
2 Items that come with the meal
4 Menu with separately priced items *(4 words)*
5 Menu used for a set length of time *(2 words)*
6 Menu of complete meals for a set price *(3 words)*
7 Main dish
8 Listings of basic breakfast items only *(2 words)*

Culinary Vocabulary Skills

Word Challenge 12-2

Directions: Rearrange each set of letters to form a word. When all the correct words are in place, you will see the vocabulary word in the shaded column.

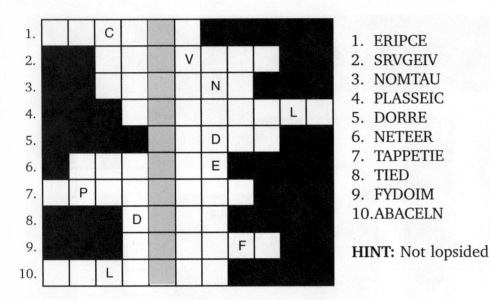

1. ERIPCE
2. SRVGEIV
3. NOMTAU
4. PLASSEIC
5. DORRE
6. NETEER
7. TAPPETIE
8. TIED
9. FYDOIM
10. ABACELN

HINT: Not lopsided

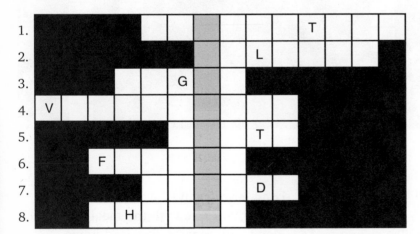

1. DONCEMTIAI
2. LESISNL
3. GASUR
4. ABSLGEEVET
5. TAMES
6. STIRUF
7. SADBER
8. CEEHES

HINT: Medical condition

Culinary Vocabulary Skills

Word Challenge 12-3

Directions: Complete the crossword puzzle using the vocabulary clues provided below.

Across

3 Menus handed to customers *(2 words)*
7 Items made from leftovers

Down

1 List of offerings fastened to menus *(2 words)*
2 First course of small portions
4 Folded cards listing daily specials *(2 words)*
5 Menu displayed on a wall or easel *(2 words)*
6 Food options announced by the server *(2 words)*

Word Challenge 12-4

Directions: Complete the crossword puzzle using the vocabulary clues provided below.

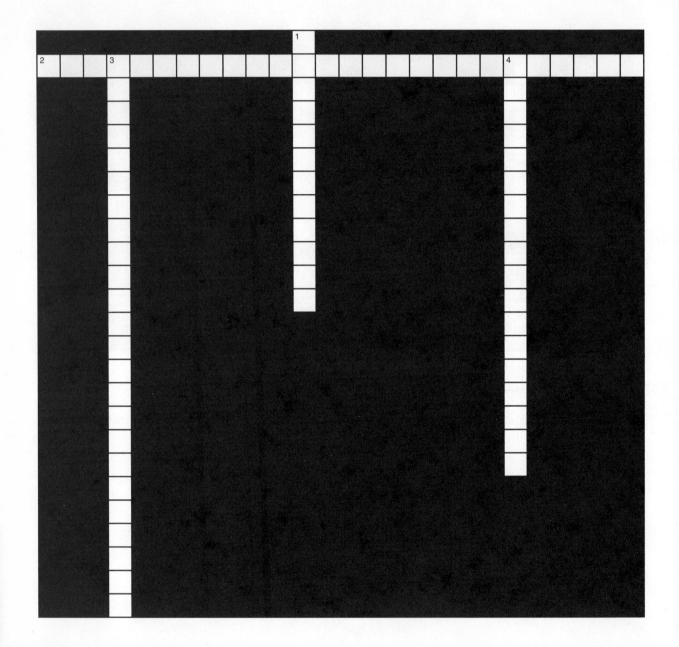

Across

2   Pricing based on customer reactions
    (3 words)

Down

1   Pricing based on past profit experience
    (2 words)
3   Pricing based on rivals' prices *(3 words)*
4   Pricing based on the profit desired
    (5 words)

Word Challenge 13-1

Directions: Complete the crossword puzzle using the vocabulary clues provided below.

Across

3 Food preparation instructions for consistent quality and quantity *(2 words)*
6 Servings produced by a recipe
7 Precise bakeshop recipe

Down

1 System to ensure standards are met *(2 words)*
2 Ingredient's percentage of a formula's flour weight *(2 words)*
4 Directions for preparing a dish
5 Amount of a serving *(2 words)*

Word Challenge 13-2

Directions: Complete the crossword puzzle using the vocabulary clues provided below.

Across

3 Recipe altered to obtain a new yield
 (2 words)
7 Number of recipe items

Down

1 How heavy a substance is
2 Substance's total space
4 Quotient of desired yield over recipe yield
 (2 words)
5 Liquid-measuring devices *(2 words)*
6 Water loss during cooking

Word Challenge 14-1

Directions: Complete the crossword puzzle using the vocabulary clues provided below.

Across

2 Item's bulk cost *(3 words)*
8 Ratio of edible portion to quantity purchased *(2 words)*
10 Price of an item *(2 words)*

Down

1 Large amount of a food
3 Written product description
4 Expense of a single serving *(3 words)*
5 Weight of a single serving *(2 words)*
6 Amount consumable after preparation *(2 words)*
7 Amount of food after preparation *(2 words)*
9 Material removed from a food product *(2 words)*

Word Challenge 14-2

Directions: Complete the crossword puzzle using the vocabulary clues provided below.

Across

1 List of everything on hand *(2 words)*
4 Ordering based on estimated periodic use *(2 words)*
7 Quick-to-spoil foods containing a breakdown inhibitor

Down

1 Ever-updated record of on-hand stock
2 Materials not to be eaten
3 Stock rotation system *(4 words)*
4 Supplies needed between deliveries
5 Invoice used to track inventory
6 Moving food from storage to the kitchen as needed

Word Challenge 15-1

Directions: Complete the crossword puzzle using the vocabulary clues provided below.

Across

2 Cooking using dry heat *(3 words)*
4 Cell components that impart color
5 Process of cooking sugar to high temperatures
6 Use of moist and dry cooking *(2 words)*

Down

1 Cooking with liquids *(3 words)*
3 Moisture escapes
7 Change from a liquid to a solid

Culinary Vocabulary Skills

Word Challenge 15-2

Directions: Complete the crossword puzzle using the vocabulary clues provided below.

Across

2 Mixture of dry and liquid ingredients
4 Cooking in a moderate amount of heated fat *(2 words)*
6 Cooking that occurs after removal from heat source *(2 words)*
8 Quickly browned
9 Cooking in a wok *(2 words)*
10 Dry cooking under heat
11 Quick cooking using a little fat

Down

1 Submerged in fat heated to 350°F *(2 words)*
2 Coating with a mixture of crumbs and eggs
3 When fat reaches preset temperature after submerging food *(2 words)*
5 Coating with flour or crumbs
7 Cooking on a skewer over heat *(3 words)*

Word Challenge 15-3

Directions: Complete the crossword puzzle using the vocabulary clues provided below.

Across

2 Cooking in a closed container with steam
3 Cooking by searing and simmering
7 Partially cooking in boiling water

Down

1 To cook liquid in a pan after removing food
2 Cooking in a nonboiling liquid
4 Cooking by searing, then submerging
5 Heated liquid rises to the top of the pan
6 Partially cooking by boiling
7 Cooking in a liquid at 150°F to 185°F

Word Challenge 16-1

Directions: Complete the crossword puzzle using the vocabulary clues provided below.

Across

2 Used to improve flavors, not change them
  (2 words)
8 Flavorings that blend with natural fibers

Down

1 Shavings of fruit rind
2 Ingredients that change food taste
3 Concentrated liquid flavorings
4 Leaves and stems that add flavor
5 Ingredients that change the flavor of foods
6 Mixtures of herbs, spices, and seeds
7 White membrane of fruits

Word Challenge 16-2

Directions: Complete the crossword puzzle using the vocabulary clues provided below.

Across

3 Italian rice dish *(2 words)*
5 Pleasing smell

Down

1 Tied herb bundle *(2 words)*
2 Spanish rice dish
4 Tied cheesecloth bag of blends

Word Challenge 16-3

Directions: Complete the crossword puzzle using the vocabulary clues provided below.

Across

2 Food accompaniments
4 Chopped, pickled items

Down

1 Chemically changed by brine
3 Condiment made of chiles and tomatoes

Word Challenge 16-4

Directions: Complete the crossword puzzle using the vocabulary clues provided below.

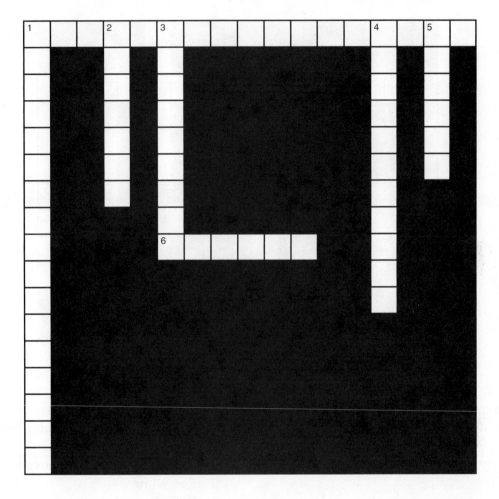

Across

1 Ears, eyes, nose, mouth, and skin at work *(2 words)*
6 Flavorful

Down

1 Systematic tasting *(2 words)*
2 Things that cause a response
3 Cells that detect stimuli
4 Clear
5 Cloudy

Word Challenge 17-1

Directions: Complete the crossword puzzle using the vocabulary clues provided below.

Across

3 Prepared and delivered breads *(3 words)*

Down

1 Absorbs flavors and loses moisture
2 Heated to destroy harmful bacteria
3 Small ceramic bowls
4 Item after water is removed
5 Egg white
6 Puffed egg dishes

Word Challenge 17-2

Directions: Rearrange each set of letters to form a word. When all the correct words are in place, you will see the vocabulary word in the shaded column.

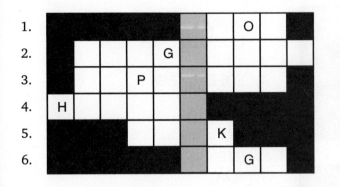

1. OCOK
2. GECTULAOA
3. ATEAPERS
4. EHOATE
5. KIML
6. SEGG

HINT: Separate

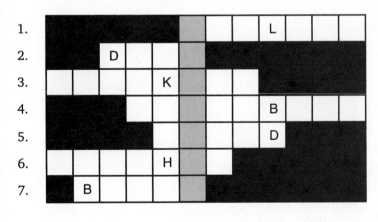

1. HELDELS
2. HIDS
3. KERMANSI
4. BAMSCELRD
5. ERFID
6. HOPCADE
7. ABDEK

HINT: Style of egg preparation

Word Challenge 17-3

Directions: Rearrange each set of letters to form a word. When all the correct words are in place, you will see the vocabulary word in the shaded column.

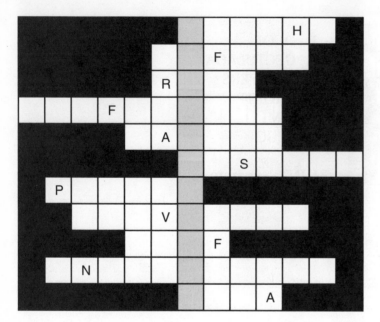

1. CHIQUE
2. UFIMFN
3. SIRE
4. FOFECCKEEA
5. GINABK
6. BUCSITI
7. DROPEW
8. EVENINLGA
9. FOAL
10. GNEDSTNIRIE
11. ADOS

HINT: Made without yeast

1. SJAM
2. CIQUK
3. HOKPESAB
4. SAINSIR
5. TURBET
6. SAKREBFAT

HINT: Rich biscuits

Word Challenge 18-1

Directions: Complete the crossword puzzle using the vocabulary clues provided below.

Across

4 Chef in charge of cold food preparation
   (2 words)

Down

1 Oblong, 7-sided vegetable cut
2 Shaped food purée
3 Team of foodservice specialists

Word Challenge 18-2

Directions: Complete the crossword puzzle using the vocabulary clues provided below.

Across

2 Curly-leafed cabbage
4 Grilled or fried bits of bread
5 Salad sauce

Down

1 Red-leafed cabbage-like plant
3 Baby greens and arugula mixture

Culinary Vocabulary Skills

Word Challenge 18-3

Directions: Complete the crossword puzzle using the vocabulary clues provided below.

Across

2   Coagulated milk liquid
4   Healthful bacteria changing the texture and flavor of cheese
6   Additive that combines unmixable liquids
7   Mixed-variety cheese *(3 words)*

Down

1   Stacking and turning cheese slabs
3   Outer surface of cheese
5   Ripened-unripened cheese combination *(2 words)*

Word Challenge 18-4

Directions: Complete the crossword puzzle using the vocabulary clues provided below.

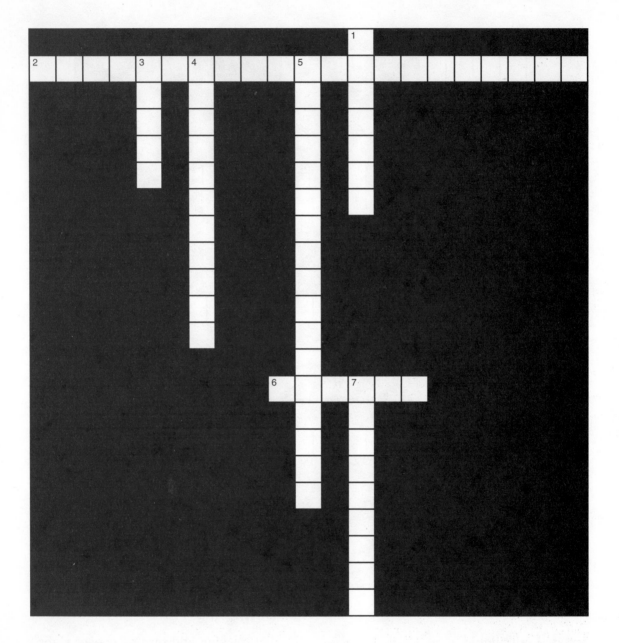

Across

2 Individual appetizer items *(3 words)*
6 Small open-face sandwich

Down

1 French for "raw"
3 Ingrediant added for appearance and texture
4 Self-service appetizers *(2 words)*
5 One-person plate of appetizers *(2 words)*
7 Italian for "before pasta"

Culinary Vocabulary Skills

Word Challenge 19-1

Directions: Complete the crossword puzzle using the vocabulary clues provided below.

Across

2 Flat-topped sandwich bread
3 Small, thin pancakes

Down

1 Flavored Italian bread
2 Pastry that can be used to create sandwich wraps
4 Fresh sauce with olive oil, basil, and garlic

Word Challenge 19-2

Directions: Rearrange each set of letters to form a word. When all the correct words are in place, you will see the vocabulary word in the shaded column.

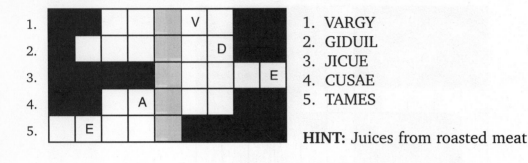

1. VARGY
2. GIDUIL
3. JICUE
4. CUSAE
5. TAMES

HINT: Juices from roasted meat

1. CLOD
2. TIPLRE
3. CHULN
4. BADER
5. ECESEH
6. TAME
7. IDEMCOTNN
8. AREDPS
9. WESGED
10. GINSILFL
11. ECLETUT
12. SICKTOHPOT

HINT: A triple-decker

Word Challenge 20-1

Directions: Complete the crossword puzzle using the vocabulary clues provided below.

Across

2 Acidic fish stock
4 Stock evaporation process
6 Liquids for soups

Down

1 Concentrated stock
3 Chopped vegetable-herb mixture
5 Powdered stock

Word Challenge 20-2

Directions: Complete the crossword puzzle using the vocabulary clues provided below.

Across

1 Five basic sauces (*2 words*)
3 Flavored, thickened liquids
4 Food processed into a smooth pulp
7 Process for moistening starch

Down

2 Sauce ingredient added for body (*2 words*)
5 Cooked fat and flour mixture
6 Puréed fruit sauce

Word Challenge 21-1

Directions: Complete the crossword puzzle using the vocabulary clues provided below.

Across

3 Clear, rich soup
4 Cooking vegetables in fat over low heat to release moisture
6 To remove particles that float to the top of soup

Down

1 Creamy, thick, shellfish soup
2 Cold potato-leek soup
3 Thickened fish soup
5 Impurities that rise to the top of the broth

Word Challenge 21-2

Directions: Complete the crossword puzzle using the vocabulary clues provided below.

Across

4   First course

Down

1   Hand-carried appetizer service
2   Bacon-wrapped appetizer
3   Small skewers of meat and vegetables

Word Challenge 22-1

Directions: Complete the crossword puzzle using the vocabulary clues provided below.

Across

1 Fish without gills and entrails
2 Meat cut from the sides of fish
3 Cut-open, dressed fish
6 Food in a sealed container without air *(2 words)*

Down

1 Drawn fish with waste removed
4 Discoloration of frozen food *(2 words)*
5 Loss of moisture as food thaws *(2 words)*

Word Challenge 22-2

Directions: Complete the crossword puzzle using the vocabulary clues provided below.

Across

1 Soft-bodied shellfish
4 Two-shelled mollusk
5 Out of the shell
8 French for "snails"
9 Italian for "squid"
10 Shaped fish mixture

Down

2 Single-shelled mollusk
3 Thin, internal-shelled mollusk
6 Hard-shelled, jointed shellfish
7 To remove a shrimp's intestines

Word Challenge 22-3

Directions: Rearrange each set of letters to form a word. When all the correct words are in place, you will see the vocabulary word in the shaded column.

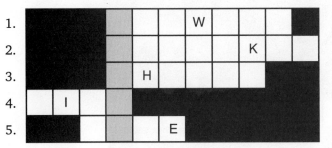

1. WASEDEE
2. KODONUCE
3. PHASED
4. SHIF
5. ICER

HINT: Rolled delicacy

1. SAMET
2. RAPMENCHT
3. RAPREPD
4. CAUSES
5. APPER
6. ISFH
7. LEBSETAEVE
8. FELLISHHS
9. VENO
10. STUBTER
11. SHBER

HINT: Fancy seafood preparation

Word Challenge 23-1

Directions: Complete the crossword puzzle using the vocabulary clues provided below.

Across

2 Ready-to-cook
3 Holds muscle fiber together *(2 words)*

Down

1 Purchase-ready poultry *(2 words)*
4 Tying poultry legs and wings

Word Challenge 23-2

Directions: Rearrange each set of letters to form a word. When all the correct words are in place, you will see the vocabulary word in the shaded column.

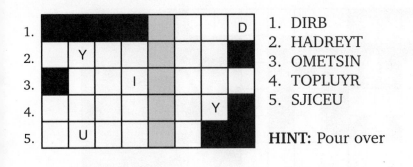

1. DIRB
2. HADREYT
3. OMETSIN
4. TOPLUYR
5. SJICEU

HINT: Pour over

1. PYSRIC
2. WROBN
3. DRIEF
4. STAF
5. SOIL
6. CYIJU
7. TPTRMREEAAEU
8. HATE
9. AFT
10. GREBNAID
11. PEDESY
12. HICCNEK
13. RIDENN
14. AGSEER

HINT: Cooking method

Culinary Vocabulary Skills

Word Challenge 24-1

Directions: Complete the crossword puzzle using the vocabulary clues provided below.

Across

1 Fat that surrounds muscle tissue
5 Percentage of food loss
7 Wrapping meat with bacon
9 Hard yellow tissue

Down

2 Meat source of gelatin
3 Adding fat strips into meat
4 Muscle-tissue fat
6 Large pieces of meat *(2 words)*
8 Menu-sized meat portions *(2 words)*

Name_____   Date _____

Word Challenge 24-2

Directions: Complete the crossword puzzle using the vocabulary clues provided below.

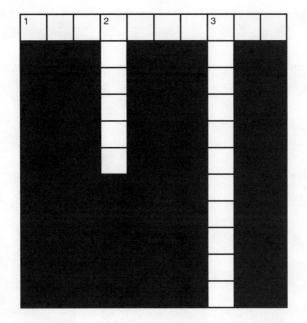

Across

1   Artificially changing food

Down

2   Preserving meat
3   Process that eliminates harmful bacteria

Word Challenge 24-3

Directions: Complete the crossword puzzle using the vocabulary clues provided below.

Across

3 Cooking at high temperatures *(3 words)*

Down

1 A concentrated brown stock that has been reduced

2 Cooking at low temperatures *(3 words)*

4 Direction of muscle fibers

Word Challenge 25-1

Directions: Complete the crossword puzzle using the vocabulary clues provided below.

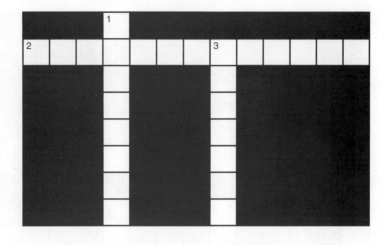

Across

2   High-protein wheat flour *(2 words)*

Down

1   Food-draining container
3   To the bite *(2 words)*

Word Challenge 25-2

Directions: Complete the crossword puzzle using the vocabulary clues provided below.

Across

2 Butter-sautéed rice dish
3 Partially cooked, dried rice *(2 words)*
5 Nutrient-coated rice *(2 words)*

Down

1 Dehulled rice *(2 words)*
3 Cooked cornmeal dish
4 Sautéed way of cooking grains *(2 words)*
6 Dried, lye-soaked corn
7 Continuous-stirring while cooking grain *(2 words)*

Name_____ Date _____

Word Challenge 26-1

Directions: Complete the crossword puzzle using the vocabulary clues provided below.

Across

2 Add water to
4 Chemicals in food that may fight disease
9 French for "melted"
10 Shrink-wrapped food items

Down

1 Fruits with stones
3 Deep-stemmed serving dish
5 Syrup-cooked fruits
6 Emitted by ripening fruit *(2 words)*
7 Spiced fruit condiment
8 Produce shipping containers

Word Challenge 26-2

Directions: Complete the crossword puzzle using the vocabulary clues provided below.

Across

2 Tied vegetable bundle
3 Liquid protector of a food product
   (2 words)
6 Hand-operated vegetable slicer
7 Low-starch potato type
8 Fleshy underground plant stem

Down

1 Potato toxin
4 Potatoes with thick skins and starchy flesh
5 Food weight without packing *(2 words)*

Name_____ Date_____

Word Challenge 26-3

Directions: Complete the crossword puzzle using the vocabulary clues provided below.

Across

3   Soaked legumes

Down

1   To cover legumes with boiling water
    (2 words)
2   Double-seamed pods containing a single
    row of seeds
3   Dried legume seeds

Word Challenge 27-1

Directions: Complete the crossword puzzle using the vocabulary clues provided below.

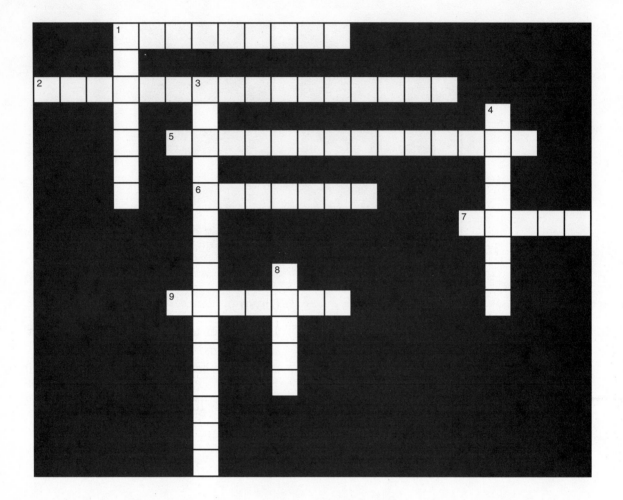

Across

1 Oven with many insulated shelves
   (2 words)
2 Ingredient's percentage of a formula's flour
   weight *(2 words)*
5 Oven with a circulating fan *(2 words)*
6 Precise bakeshop recipe
7 Shaped pans
9 Weighing bakeshop ingredients

Down

1 Machine used to roll out dough
3 Food container that controls
   temperature and humidity *(2 words)*
4 Ferris-wheel-type oven
8 Bottomless baking containers

Culinary Vocabulary Skills

Word Challenge 27-2

Directions: Complete the crossword puzzle using the vocabulary clues provided below.

Across

3 Solid baking fat
7 Yeast breakdown process
9 Elastic substance in baked products
11 Concentrated liquid flavorings

Down

1 Causes baked goods to rise *(2 words)*
2 Bread's outer surface
4 Adding hydrogen to change oil into solid fat
5 Process of losing moisture
6 Mixture that's drier than a batter
8 Baked product's texture
10 Mixture of dry and liquid ingredients that is easy to pour

Word Challenge 28-1

Directions: Complete the crossword puzzle using the vocabulary clues provided below.

Across

1 Initial mixture of warm liquid and yeast
3 Elastic, easily-torn dough *(3 words)*
5 Baker's wooden board

Down

1 High-fat, high-sugar dough *(3 words)*
2 Fat-layered dough *(5 words)*
4 Low-fat, low-sugar dough *(3 words)*
6 Causes dough to rise

Word Challenge 28-2

Directions: Complete the crossword puzzle using the vocabulary clues provided below.

Across

4 Holding dough for baking the next day
6 Forming dough into distinctive shapes
8 Stage allowing yeast to become its strongest
9 Rapid rise of a yeast product during baking *(2 words)*

Down

1 When dough ingredients break down *(2 words)*
2 Proofing stage when gluten relaxes *(2 words)*
3 Working dough
4 Turning in dough sides and then turning dough over
5 Placing shaped dough in pans
6 Making shallow cuts in baked goods
7 Making surface holes before baking

Word Challenge 29-1

Directions: Complete the crossword puzzle using the vocabulary clues provided below.

Across

2   Thin batter *(2 words)*

Down

1   Thick batter *(2 words)*
3   Large irregular holes

Word Challenge 29-2

Directions: Rearrange each set of letters to form a word. When all the correct words are in place, you will see the vocabulary word in the shaded column.

1. BREAK
2. CUNGTIT
3. STCUR
4. RIPECE
5. SAMRVEE
6. SIRES
7. HOTSINGENR
8. IXINMG
9. DENTIEGINR
10. LAST
11. HATE
12. FUROL
13. RDY

HINT: To cut-in fat

1. OGDUH
2. CAPSEE
3. RUFOL
4. CEALLOCP
5. ARBDES
6. ARTETB
7. GEGS

HINT: Let the air out

Word Challenge 29-3

Directions: Rearrange each set of letters to form a word. When all the correct words are in place, you will see the vocabulary word in the shaded column.

1. OWLB
2. FOLUR
3. RABEK
4. OPONSS
5. GINPENSERIT
6. QUILID
7. SPAN
8. GAURS
9. NIBMOCE
10. KEAC
11. RUXEMIT
12. OHETEGTR
13. DOWREP
14. TEDRESS

HINT: Mixing oil and flour

1. RINPIECOTS
2. ICREEP
3. SONDFEET
4. SFAT
5. EXRIM
6. GHILT
7. QUEITCENH
8. RUAGS
9. KLIM
10. NOVE
11. SESTP
12. SHAKEBOP
13. REDROPCUE
14. SEBRAD

HINT: Mixing shortening and sugar

Word Challenge 30-1

Directions: Complete the crossword puzzle using the vocabulary clues provided below.

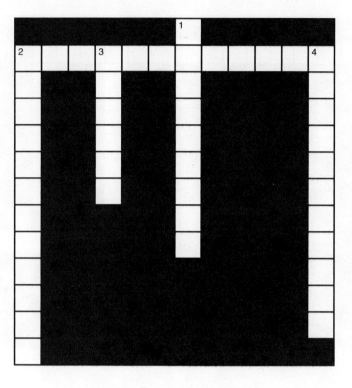

Across

2 Low-moisture batter cookies *(2 words)*

Down

1 To stack identical cookie pans *(2 words)*
2 High-sugar, low-fat cookies *(2 words)*
3 Expand
4 Low-sugar, low-fat, high-liquid cookies *(2 words)*

Word Challenge 30-2

Directions: Complete the crossword puzzle using the vocabulary clues provided below.

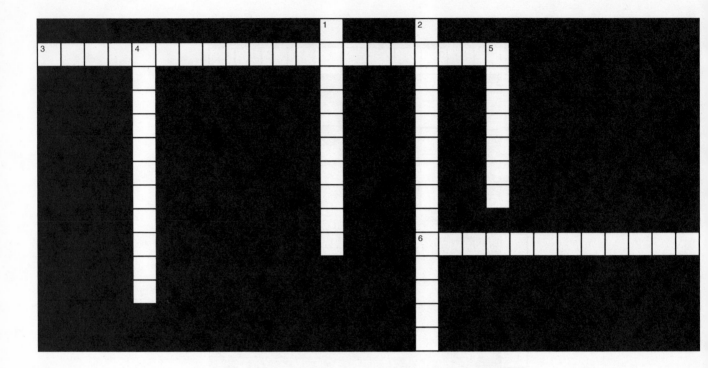

Across

3 Fat used to create a smooth consistency *(2 words)*
6 Cakes containing whipped egg-whites *(2 words)*

Down

1 Cakes with equal parts of butter, flour, sugar, and eggs *(2 words)*
4 Cakes containing whipped eggs *(3 words)*
5 European sponge cake

Word Challenge 30-3

Directions: Complete the crossword puzzle using the vocabulary clues provided below.

Across

3 Preparing pie shells in advance *(2 words)*

Down

1 Stiffly beaten egg white and sugar mixture

2 Making folds around pie crust edge

Word Challenge 30-4

Directions: Complete the crossword puzzle using the vocabulary clues provided below.

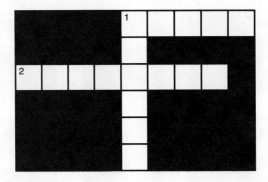

Across

1 Heat a liquid just below the boiling point
2 Creamy gelatin dessert with custard sauce

Down

1 Frozen fruit-juice dessert

Unit 1 Word Challenge

Directions: Complete the crossword puzzle using the vocabulary clues provided below.

Across

5 A folded napkin placed on a dinner or service plate used for carrying flatware
6 An organization of workers in a similar field
8 Making use of all your personal connections to achieve your career goals
11 A common form of ownership used by chain restaurants in which a franchise company sells the business owner the rights to its name, logo, concept, and products
13 The skill of putting yourself in another's place
16 A branched candlestick
17 A half-size cup in which espresso is traditionally served
18 At the table
19 A beverage made by forcing hot water and steam through finely ground, dark-roasted coffee beans
20 A device that holds a large pan of food over a canned heat source

Down

1 To set items on the table before food is served
2 A company that sells products to the foodservice industry
3 The support of customers
4 The "under" chef who reports to the executive chef
7 Products that can spoil quickly, even when stored correctly
9 A formal meeting between you and your potential employer
10 A legal association of two or more people who share the ownership of the business
12 Your internal guidelines for distinguishing right from wrong
14 The process of promoting and supplying goods and services to customers
15 To extract the flavors of a substance by placing it in a hot liquid

Culinary Vocabulary Skills

Unit 2 Word Challenge

Directions: Complete the crossword puzzle using the vocabulary clues provided on the next page.

Culinary Vocabulary Skills

Copyright © Glencoe/McGraw-Hill, a division of The McGraw-Hill Companies, Inc.

Unit 2 Word Challenge

Directions: Complete the crossword puzzle using the vocabulary clues provided below.

Across

1 Anticipating future business needs, such as what things will cost, how much money will be needed, what staffing needs there will be, and what profits will be expected

4 The path food takes from receiving to disposal where hazards can be controlled and dangers minimized

6 Heating products at very high temperatures to destroy harmful bacteria

7 Products that can spoil quickly, even when stored correctly

10 Or adjusted; a food thermometer should be adjusted before each shift or each delivery, and if it is dropped

13 The science concerned with the efficient and safe interaction between people and the things in their environment

17 Harmful organisms or substances

18 Applying specific standards of quality to food products

19 The people who will be a business's main customers

20 The process of making a new employee familiar with a foodservice organization, its policies and procedures, and specific job duties

Down

2 Waste that includes packaging material, containers, and recyclables

3 A worker who is in direct contact with food

5 Scheduling too many people to work on a given shift

8 A deep cut or tear in the skin, such as a knife wound

9 A wound in which a portion of the skin is partially or completely torn off, such as a severed finger

11 The unfair treatment of people based on age, race, gender, ethnicity, religion, physical appearance, disability, or other factors

12 Rules by which government agencies enforce minimum standards of quality

14 Materials that are quick-to-burn

15 Healthy or clean and whole; healthy and sanitary conditions and effective sanitary practices

16 Free or low-cost efforts of a facility to improve its image

Unit 3 Word Challenge

Directions: Complete the crossword puzzle using the vocabulary clues provided on the next page.

Unit 3 Word Challenge

Directions: Complete the crossword puzzle using the vocabulary clues provided below.

Across

3 The body's main source of energy, or fuel

5 Or spec; a written description of the products a foodservice operation needs to purchase

6 A half-size refrigerator unit that fits under the counter in each individual work station

9 Vegetarians who include eggs in addition to foods from plant sources in their diets

11 The number of servings, or portions, that a recipe produces

12 People who do not eat any meat or animal products

15 The number of individual items used in a recipe to indicate the size of each item

17 Arrangement of the kitchen equipment

22 A pricing method based on how a customer reacts to menu prices that is used once the selling price of a menu item is determined

23 The process of using a steel to keep a knife blade straight and to smooth out any irregularities; after the knife has been sharpened

24 A French term that means "to put in place"

Down

1 The percentage of food lost during its storage and preparation; the loss of water in meat as it cooks

2 A special type of recipe used in the bakeshop that includes the precise amount of each ingredient

4 The consumable food product that remains after preparation

7 Perishable items that contain an inhibitor that slows down the chemical breakdown of the food. These products include smoked fish, processed meats, and pickled vegetables.

8 The part of the blade that continues into the knife's handle

10 A common pricing method for restaurants with successful past performance records in which the food cost percent is divided into 100%. The resulting factor is multiplied by the cost of the menu item, giving the menu selling price.

13 A sharpening stone used to keep knives sharp

14 Disk-shaped slices made from cylindrical fruits or vegetables such as cucumbers or carrots; also called round

16 Items that come with the meal, such as a choice of potato, rice, or pasta and a choice of vegetable

18 The amount of stock needed to cover a facility from one delivery to the next

19 A piece of equipment used to keep foods, such as sauces and soups, warm so they can be used in other dishes; also referred to as a water bath

20 Substances added to foods to improve them in some way

21 A menu that is used for a set period of time, such as a week, a month, or even longer

Name_____ Date _____

Unit 4 Word Challenge

Directions: Complete the crossword puzzle using the vocabulary clues provided on the next page.

Culinary Vocabulary Skills

Unit 4 Word Challenge

Directions: Complete the crossword puzzle using the vocabulary clues provided below.

Across

2   A type of meal service in which appetizers are carried on a serving plate at a standing event

4   An uncooked sauce made of olive oil, pine nuts or walnuts, a hard cheese such as parmesan, and fresh basil, garlic, salt, and pepper

6   A process in which slabs of cheese are stacked and turned

9   A cold version of potato-leek soup

10 Rice that has had the hull, or outer covering, removed

12 Eggs that are covered with cream or milk and sometimes bread crumbs. They are prepared in ramekins lined with a variety of ingredients.

14 The process in which starch granules absorb moisture when placed in a liquid

19 An Italian bread flavored with olive oil and herbs

20 A cabbagelike plant with a slightly bitter, red leaf

21 The process of wrapping a lean meat with fat, such as bacon, before roasting

Down

1   Tying the legs and wings against a bird's body to allow for even cooking and to create an attractive final product when served

3   The separation of eggs and solids, resulting in a tough yet watery egg dish

5   An ingredient, such as cornstarch, that adds body to a sauce

7   "To the bite"; to cook pasta so that it is not too soft or overdone

8   Natural chemicals found in fruits, vegetables, grains, and dry beans that seem to have anti-cancer properties

11 The tissue that holds muscle fiber together

12 Things that cause an activity or response

13 The process of cooking sugar to high temperatures

15 A type of processing that eliminates potentially harmful microorganisms and enhances food safety

16 To shrink-wrap food items for purchasing and shipping

17 To coat foods with flour or finely ground crumbs

18 A Spanish rice dish with meat or shellfish

Unit 5 Word Challenge

Directions: Complete the crossword puzzle using the vocabulary clues provided below.

Across

2 A method of mixing that involves cutting in fat with dry ingredients
3 The internal texture of a baked product
8 A frozen dessert made up of fruit juices, sugar, and water
9 A type of container that has no bottom and is used to produce round or square breads or baked dessert items
10 Causes dough to rise as it fills with carbon dioxide bubbles
12 Weighing bakeshop ingredients
13 A mixture of sugar and stiffly beaten egg whites
14 A mixture that contains less liquid than batters, making it easy to work with your hands
15 Large irregular holes

Down

1 A mixture of flour, yeast, and a warm liquid that begins the leavening action
4 Batters that are so thick they need to be scraped or dropped from a portion or ice cream scoop to the cookware
5 A mixing method that involves using oil or liquid fat to blend ingredients
6 To work dough until it is smooth and elastic
7 A type of dough that consists of 0-1% fat and sugar
8 Expand
11 To heat a liquid to just below the boiling point

Culinary Vocabulary Skills

CULINARY VOCABULARY SKILLS
ANSWER KEY

Word Challenge 1-1

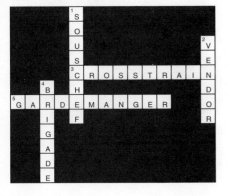

Across: CROSSTRAIN, GARDEMANGER
Down: SOUSCHEF, VENDOR, BRIGADE

Word Challenge 1-2

FINEDINING, NONCOMMERCIALOPERATIONS, QUICKSERVICE, COMMERCIALOPERATIONS, COUNTRYLEVEL, CLOSESERVICE, TRENDS

Word Challenge 1-3

APPLICATION, LETTER, MENTOR, EVALUATE, QUALIFY, CERTIFIED, FORMS, INTERVIEW, TEACHER, TRAINING, REGULATIONS, PRACTICE, DIPLOMA, ATTENDANCE

LEARN, APPLY, APPRENTICE, PROFESSION, PROGRAM, FREE, EMPLOYEE, ASSIGNMENT, STANDARD, HYGIENE, APPEARANCE, RESUME

Word Challenge 1-4

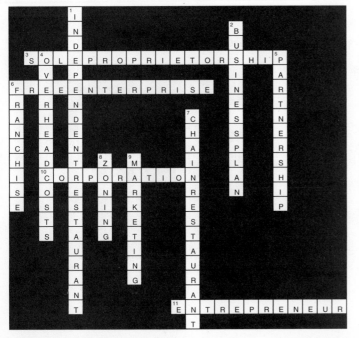

INDIVIDUAL, SOLEPROPRIETORSHIP, BUSINESS, PARTNERSHIP, FREEENTERPRISE, CHAIN, FRANCHISE, CORPORATION, ZONING, MARKETING, RESTAURANT, ENTREPRENEUR

Word Challenge 2-1

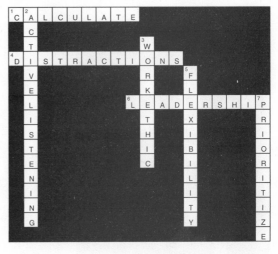

CALCULATE, WORK, DISTRACTIONS, LEADERSHIP, ACTIVELISTENING, FLEXIBILITY, PRIORITIZE, ETHICS

Word Challenge 2-2

(Crossword) Across/Down answers visible: JOB, JOBLEAD, JOBINTERVIEW, KEYWORDS, TRADEPUBLICATIONS, RÉSUMÉ, NETWORKING

Word Challenge 2-3

Answers visible: WORKERSCOMPENSATION, DISCRIMINATION, SEXUALHARASSMENT, EMPATHY, ETHICS, REPETITIVESTRESSINJURIES, PROBATION, COMPENSATORYTIME, MINIMUMWAGE, LABORUNION, DEDUCTIONS

Word Challenge 3-1

Answers visible: STATION, BODYLANGUAGE, PATRONAGE, SECTION

Word Challenge 3-2

Answers visible: COVER, APPETIZERS, USSELLING, PRESET, UNDERLINER, HIGHLIGHTING, CALLING

Word Challenge 3-3

Answers visible: CAPUCCINO, DEMITASSE, ESPRESSO, INFUSE

Word Challenge 4-1

Answers visible: FOODCOURT, FOCALPOINT, BANQUETTE, TABBED, FLAMBÉ, CAFFEINGDISH, HORSDOEUVRE, SIDE

Word Challenge 4-2

Answers visible: CENTERPIECES, CONVENIENTS, NAPKIN, SIDEWORK, SERVIETTE, PAN, FLATWARE, CANDELABRA, HEATTREATED, PERISHABLE, PRESETMENU

Word Challenge 5-1

Crossword answers:
- HUMAN RESOURCES
- PROFIT AND LOSS STATEMENT
- FORECAST
- DIRECT LABOR
- OVERSTAFFING
- BREAKEVEN
- INDIRECT LABOR

Word Challenge 5-4

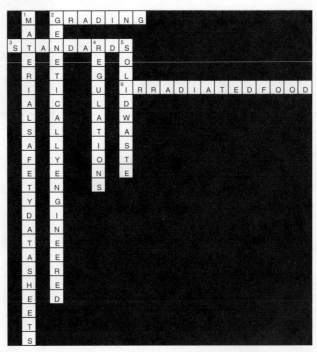

Crossword answers:
- FRANCHISE
- CHAIN
- CLIENTELE
- DIRECT MARKETING
- MARKETPLACE
- ATMOSPHERE
- POSITIONING
- COMPETITORS
- PUBLICITY
- PUBLIC RELATIONS
- ADVERTISING

Word Challenge 5-2

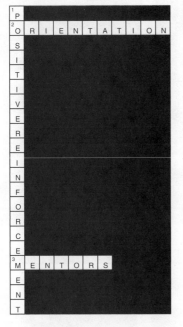

Crossword answers:
- POSITIVE REINFORCEMENT
- ORIENTATION
- MENTORS

Word Challenge 6-1

Crossword answers:
- MATERIAL SAFETY DATA SHEETS
- GRADING
- GEOTECHNICAL ENGINEERED
- STANDARDS
- REGULATIONS
- SOLID WASTE
- IRRADIATED FOOD

Word Challenge 5-3

Crossword answers:
- TURNOVER RATE
- BYPASSING
- BALANCE

Culinary Vocabulary Skills

Word Challenge 6-2

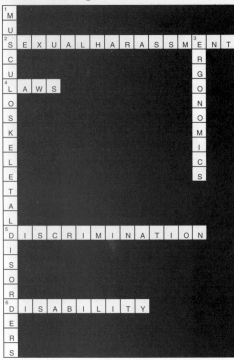

Across / Down answers:

- M U S C U L O S K E L E T A L (down, 1)
- ¹M
- ²SEXUAL HARASSMENT
- ³ERGONOMICS (down)
- ⁴LAWS
- ⁵DISCRIMINATION
- ⁶DISABILITY
- I S O R D E R S (continuing down)

Word Challenge 7-1

- ¹FLAMMABLE (down)
- ²LOCKOUTTAGOUT
- ³BRUSION (down)
- ⁴PUNCTURE (down)
- ⁵AVULSION
- ⁶HEIMLICHMANEUVER (down)
- ⁷LACERATION
- ⁸CARDIOPULMONARYRESUSCITATION

Word Challenge 7-2

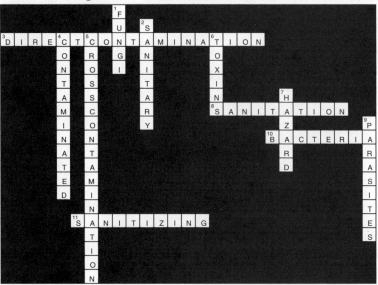

- ¹FUNGI (down)
- ²SANITARY (down)
- ³DIRECTCONTAMINATION
- ⁴CONTAMINATED (down)
- ⁵CROSSCONTAMINATION (down)
- ⁶TOXIN (down)
- ⁷HAZARD (down)
- ⁸SANITATION
- ⁹PARASITES (down)
- ¹⁰BACTERIA
- ¹¹SANITIZING

Word Challenge 8-1

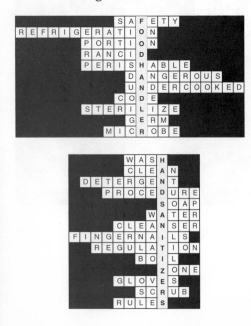

- SAFETY
- REFRIGERATION
- FOODHANDLER (down)
- PORTION
- RANCID
- PERISHABLE
- DANGEROUS
- UNDERCOOKED
- CODE
- STERILIZE
- GERM
- MICROBE

- WASH
- CLEAN
- HANDSANITIZERS (down)
- DETERGENT
- PROCEDURE
- SOAP
- WATER
- CLEANSER
- FINGERNAILS
- REGULATION
- BOX
- GLOVES
- SCRUB
- RULES

Word Challenge 8-2

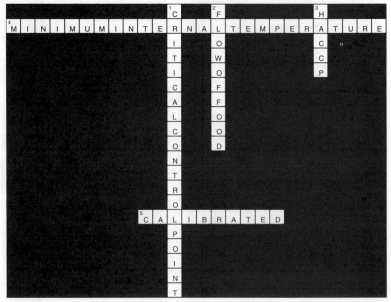

- ¹CRITICALCONTROLPOINT (down)
- ²TOWFOOD (down)
- ³HCCP (down)
- ⁴MINIMUMINTERNALTEMPERATURE
- ⁵CALIBRATED

Culinary Vocabulary Skills

Word Challenge 8-3

Word Challenge 9-1

Word Challenge 9-2

Word Challenge 9-3

Word Challenge 9-4

Word Challenge 10-1

Word Challenge 10-2

Word Challenge 11-1

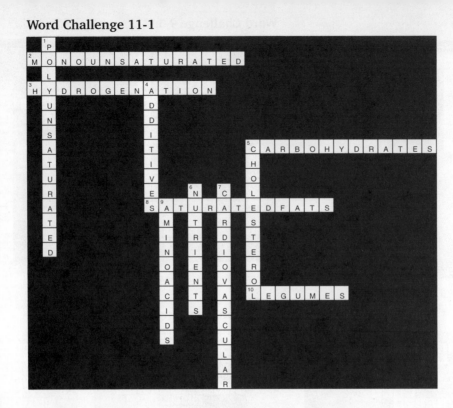

Word Challenge 11-2

Word Challenge 11-3

Culinary Vocabulary Skills

Word Challenge 12-1

1 FIX

3 SEMI À LA CARTE MENU

9 PRIX FIXE MENUS

10 MENU

Down words: FIXEDMENU, SDMENU, À LA CARTE MENU, CYCLEMENU, TABLED'HÔTEMENU, ENTRÉE, ANTIPASTS, ACCOMPANIMENTS, COTINENTALMENUS

Word Challenge 12-2

RECIPE
SERVING
PROAMOUNT
SPECIALS
ORDER
ENTREE
APPETITE
DIET
MODIFY
BALANCE

MEDICATION
ILLNESS
SUGAR
VEGETABLES
MEATS
FRUITS
BREADS
CHEESE

Word Challenge 12-3

1 CLUB

2 A

3 PRINTED MENUS

7 EXTENDERS

Down words: APPETIZERS, COUPONS, ABLENTENTS, MENUBOARD, SPOKENMENU

Word Challenge 12-4

1 F

2 PSYCHOLOGICAL PRICING METHOD

Down words: COMPETITORSPRICINGMETHOD, FACTORMETHOD, MARKUPONCOSTMETHOD

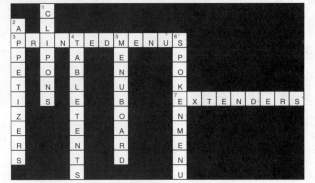

Word Challenge 13-1

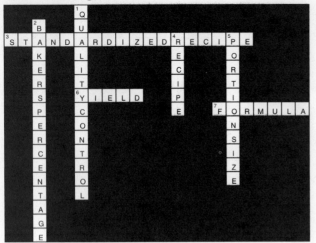

Word Challenge 13-2

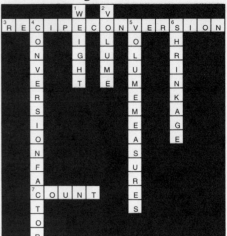

Word Challenge 14-1

Word Challenge 14-2

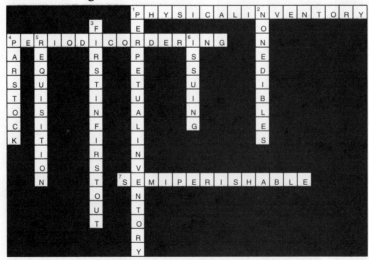

Word Challenge 15-1

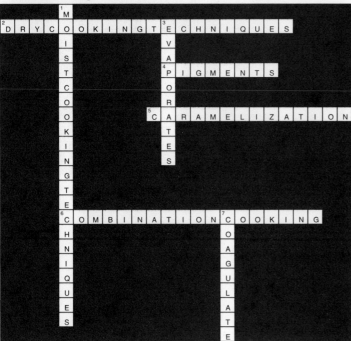

Word Challenge 15-2

Word Challenge 15-3

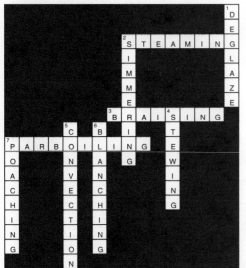

Word Challenge 16-1

Word Challenge 16-2

Word Challenge 16-3

Word Challenge 16-4

```
S E N S O R Y P E R C E P T I O N
E       T       E         R     P
N       I       C         A     A
S       M       E         N     Q
O       U       P         S     U
R       L       T         L     E
Y       I       O         U
E             6 S A V O R Y
V               R         C
A                         E
L                         N
U                         T
A
T
I
O
N
```

Word Challenge 17-1

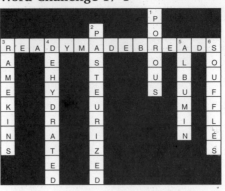

```
                              P
                  2 P         O
3 R E A D Y M A D E B R E A D S
A       4 E       S       O   O
M         H       T       U   U
E         Y       E       S   F
K         D       U           F
I         R       R       M   L
N         A       I       I   É
S         T       Z       N   S
          E       E
          D       D
```

Word Challenge 17-2

```
          C O O K
  C O A G U L A T E
  S E P A R A T E
H E A T E D   K
      M I L   E G G S
```

```
              S H E L L E D
      D I S H   H
R A M E K I N S   I N S
      S   C R A M B L E D
      F   R
      R I E D
P O A C H E D
  B A K E D
```

Word Challenge 17-3

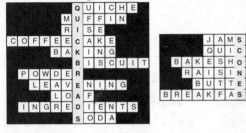

```
        Q U I C H E
      M U F F I N
      R I S E
C O F F E E C A K E
      B A K I N G
      R   B I S C U I T
P O W D E R E N I N G
  L E A V E F
      L O A D
  I N G R E D I E N T S
      S   S O D A
```

```
          J A M S
          Q U I C K
    B A K E S H O P
    R A I S I N S
      B U T T E R
B R E A K F A S T
```

Word Challenge 18-1

```
                        T
                        O
          3 B   2 Q     U
4 G A R D E M A N G E R R
A       I   U   N       É
R       N   E   G       E
N       G   E   L       D
I       A       L
S       D       E
H       E
```

Word Challenge 18-2

```
                  R
    2 K A L E      D
          D        I        3 M
        4 C R O U T O N S     E
          C        H          S
        5 D R E S S I N G      C
                   O          L
                              U
                              N
```

Word Challenge 18-3

```
    1 C
2 W H E Y
    E
    D
    D
    A      3 R
4 R I P E N I N G
  I 5 R   N
  N R O   D
  G O C
    6 E M U L S I F I E R
    S
    S
    E
    D
    7 C O L D P A C K C H E E S E
    H
    E
    E
    S
    E
```

Word Challenge 18-4

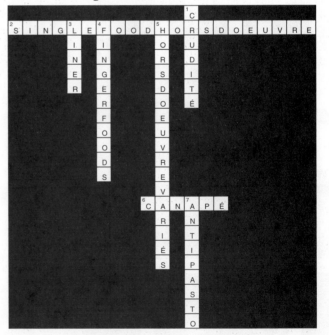

```
                      1 C
2 S I N G L E F O O D 5 H O R S D O E U V R E
        I     I       O       U
        N     N       R       D
        E     G       S       I
        R     E       D       T
              R       O       É
              F       E
              O       U
              O       V
              D       R
              S       E
                      V
              6 C A N A P É
              R       N
              I       T
              É       I
              S       P
                      A
                      S
                      T
                      O
```

Culinary Vocabulary Skills

Word Challenge 19-1

Word Challenge 19-2

Word Challenge 20-1

Word Challenge 21-2
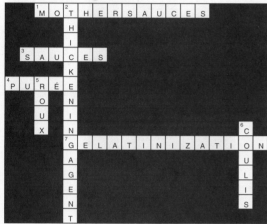

Word Challenge 21-1

Word Challenge 21-2

Word Challenge 22-1
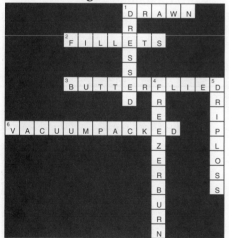

Word Challenge 22-2
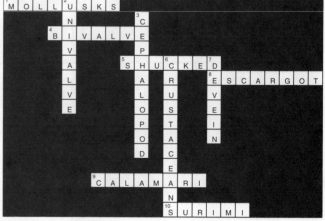

Word Challenge 22-3
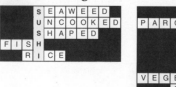

Word Challenge 23-1

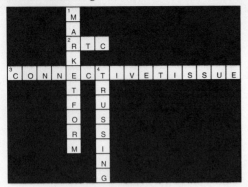

Word Challenge 23-2

Word Challenge 24-1

Word Challenge 24-2

Word Challenge 24-3

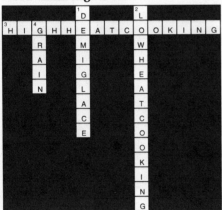

Word Challenge 25-1

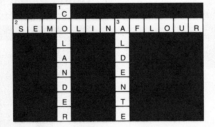

Word Challenge 25-2

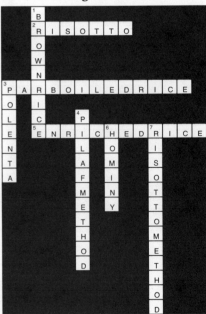

Culinary Vocabulary Skills

Word Challenge 26-1

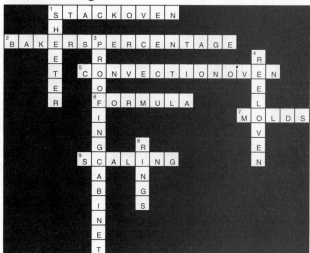

Word Challenge 26-2

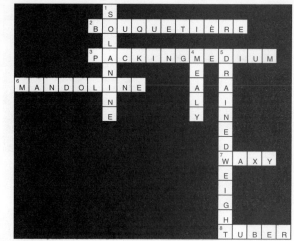

Word Challenge 26-3

Word Challenge 27-1

Word Challenge 27-2

Word Challenge 28-1

Word Challenge 28-2

Word Challenge 29-1

Word Challenge 29-2

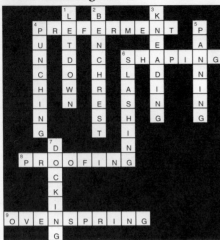

Word Challenge 29-3

Word Challenge 30-1

Word Challenge 30-2

Word Challenge 30-3

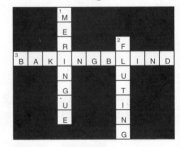

Word Challenge 30-4

Unit 1 Word Challenge

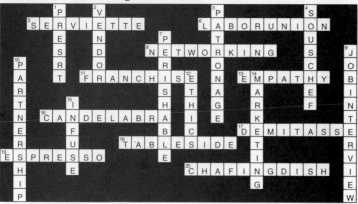

Unit 2 Word Challenge

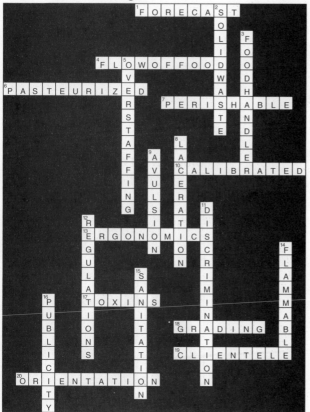

Unit 3 Word Challenge

Unit 4 Word Challenge

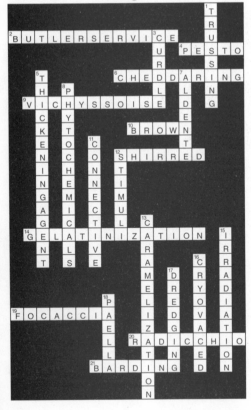

Unit 5 Word Challenge

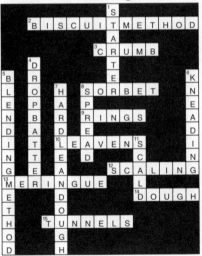

Culinary Vocabulary Skills